Language Arts

Assessments

Illustrations Credits
All illustrations © K12 unless otherwise noted

About K12 Inc.
K12 Inc. (NYSE: LRN) drives innovation and advances the quality of education by delivering state-of-the-art digital learning platforms and technology to students and school districts around the world. K12 is a company of educators offering its online and blended curriculum to charter schools, public school districts, private schools, and directly to families. More information can be found at K12.com.

978-1-60153-189-6
Printed by Action Printing, Fond du Lac, WI, USA, July 2020

Contents

Literature & Comprehension

Semester Checkpoint
Learning Coach Instructions
Reading Comprehension and Analysis

Explain that students are going to show what they have learned this semester.

1. Give students pages LC 7–LC 17 of the Semester Checkpoint.

2. Read the directions on the students' pages together. Use the Learning Coach instructions on pages LC 1–LC 6 to administer the Checkpoint.

3. Use the Answer Key to score the Checkpoint, and enter the results online.

4. Review each exercise with students. Work with students to correct any exercise they missed.

Clouds

Part 1. Book Walk Have students take you on a Book Walk of "Clouds." Ask the questions and note students' responses.

1. What kind of writing is this?

2. How is this kind of writing different from other kinds?

3. What is the title of this writing?

4. What can you use to make a prediction about this writing?

5. What prediction can you make based on what you see?

Part 2. Reading Comprehension Read the poem aloud to students, and then have students read the poem on their own. Ask the questions and note students' responses.

6. Which words rhyme in the poem?

7. Which words or phrases are repeated in the poem?

8. The speaker uses the words *white sheep* to describe something else. What is it?

9. Why might the poet choose *white sheep* as a description?

10. What does the speaker describe when she says, *When the wind stops/You all stand still*?

11. What does the speaker describe when she says, *When the wind blows/You walk away slow*?

LITERATURE & COMPREHENSION

The Bear Facts

Part 3. Book Walk Have students take you on a Book Walk of "The Bear Facts." Ask the questions and note students' responses.

12.   What kind of writing is this?

13.   How is this kind of writing different from poems and plays?

14.   What is the title?

15.   What can you use to make a prediction about this writing?

16.   What prediction can you make based on what you see?

Part 4. Reading Comprehension Read the first two paragraphs of the story aloud twice. Have students read the rest of the story on their own and answer the multiple choice questions.

LITERATURE & COMPREHENSION

Brother Rabbit Fools Brother Bear

Part 5. Book Walk Have students take you on a Book Walk of "Brother Rabbit Fools Brother Bear." Ask the questions and note students' responses.

23. What kind of writing is this?

24. How is this kind of writing different from poems and plays?

25. What is the title?

26. What can you use to make a prediction about this writing?

27. What prediction can you make based on what you see?

Part 6. Reading Comprehension Read the first three paragraphs of the story aloud twice. Have students read the rest of the story to themselves. Ask the questions and note students' responses.

28. Who are the main characters?

29. What is the setting of the story?

30. What is the proper sequence of events in the story?

31. What does Brother Rabbit think of Brother Bear?

32. What happens at the end of the story?

Part 7. Literary Analysis Have students complete the chart and answer the question about the story.

☼ Semester Checkpoint
Reading Comprehension and Analysis

Clouds

Christina Rossetti

White sheep, white sheep,
On a blue hill,
When the wind stops,
You all stand still.

When the wind blows,
You walk away slow.
White sheep, white sheep,
Where do you go?

Name _____ Date _____

Part 1. Book Walk

Do a Book Walk for "Clouds." Listen to the questions and say your answers.

1.–5.

Part 2. Reading Comprehension

Listen to the questions about "Clouds" and say your answers.

6.–11.

LITERATURE & COMPREHENSION

The Bear Facts

Have you ever had a teddy bear to cuddle and snuggle? Have you read books with a bear characters such as Little Bear, Winnie-the-Pooh, or Paddington? How cute and furry they are! How roly-poly!

But, real bears are not so sweet and cuddly. They are wild creatures, and some are very big and very powerful. A grizzly bear can weigh about 900 pounds and stand 8 feet tall. That's about as high as the ceiling in most rooms.

The American black bear, which can grow to 6 feet tall and weigh 600 pounds, is the most common bear in North America. If you and your family go camping, you might see one or hear one trying to get at your food. This bear will eat just about anything it gets its paws on, including fish, insects, pine cones, berries, and roots.

A black bear's favorite treat is honey. A black bear can use its sharp claws to rip open a tree with bees in it. The bear reaches in through the hole and pulls out the honeycomb and eats it, bees and all! Bee stings do not bother the bear very much because it has such thick fur.

Baby bears are called cubs. When a mother bear has babies, she usually has one to four cubs. A mother bear takes good care of her cubs. She teaches them how to find food. If she thinks something is a danger to her cubs, she will attack.

So, real bears are not much like teddy bears at all. Real bears are big, strong, wild creatures. They're not for cuddling and snuggling!

Part 3. Book Walk

Do a Book Walk for "The Bear Facts." Listen to the questions and say your answers.

12.–16.

Part 4. Reading Comprehension

Read the question about "The Bear Facts" and choose the answer.

17. What kind of writing is "The Bear Facts"?

   A. fiction   **C.** poetry

   B. nonfiction   **D.** drama

18. What is the topic of "The Bear Facts"?

   A. real bears   **C.** mother bears

   B. teddy bears   **D.** baby bears

19. What is the main idea of "The Bear Facts"?

   A. Teddy bears are cute and furry.

   B. Black bears will eat just about anything.

   C. Mother bears take good care of their cubs.

   D. Real bears are big, strong, wild creatures.

LITERATURE & COMPREHENSION

20. Which sentence is a fact from the article?

    A. How roly-poly!

    B. How cute and furry they are!

    C. A black bear's favorite treat is honey.

    D. Have you ever had a teddy bear to cuddle and snuggle?

21. Which sentence is an opinion from the article?

    A. How cute and furry they are!

    B. Baby bears are called cubs.

    C. A grizzly bear can weigh about 900 pounds.

    D. She teaches them how to find food.

22. What might a mother bear do for her cubs?

    A. leave them alone while she looks for food

    B. climb a tree to escape danger that comes near

    C. find the cubs a safe and warm place to sleep

    D. eat all the fish she finds so she can stay strong

Brother Rabbit Fools Brother Bear

One day, Brother Bear caught a fish from the stream. As he headed home through the woods, he smacked his big bear lips. He couldn't wait to cook that fish.

Well, sir! Brother Rabbit was hiding in the grass when Brother Bear walked by.

I sure would like to eat some fish, Brother Rabbit thought. So he took a shortcut through the woods, lay down on the path, and closed his eyes.

Brother Bear came along and said, "Oh, my. There's a tired rabbit."

Then, Brother Bear went on his way.

Brother Rabbit ran through the woods again. He threw himself down on the path and closed his eyes. Brother Bear saw him and said, "Oh, dear. There's a second tired rabbit."

Then, Brother Bear kept going.

Brother Rabbit took another shortcut through the woods. Soon, Brother Bear saw him stretched out on the path with his eyes closed.

LITERATURE & COMPREHENSION

Name .... Date ....

"I'll go get the other two rabbits," Brother Bear said to himself. "I'll take all three home and keep them as servants."

So, Brother Bear laid down his fish. He went back along the path, but he found no rabbits. And, when he came back for his fish, it was gone, too!

Brother Bear looked around. Brother Rabbit was standing in the path with a big cooking spoon. He was stirring soup in an iron pot over a fire.

"I smell fish!" Brother Bear said.

"Naw," said Brother Rabbit. "You smell turnip greens and bacon."

"My nose knows what it knows!" Brother Bear roared. He grabbed the spoon and brought up fish from the bottom of the pot.

Brother Rabbit ran off into the woods. "See you later, Brother Bear!" he called from behind a tree.

Brother Bear chased Brother Rabbit, but he never did catch him. No one ever catches Brother Rabbit. No, sir!

Part 5. Book Walk

Do a Book Walk for "Brother Rabbit Fools Brother Bear." Listen to the questions and say your answers.

23.–27.

Part 6. Reading Comprehension

Listen to the questions about "Brother Rabbit Fools Brother Bear" and say your answers.

28.–32.

Part 7. Literary Analysis

Complete the chart and answer the question about "Brother Rabbit Fools Brother Bear."

33.

Brother Rabbit's Choice	What Brother Rabbit Chooses	Consequence of This Choice
Whether or not to trick Brother Bear to get the fish	Brother Rabbit decides to	Brother Bear
Whether or not to run away with the fish or trick Brother Bear again	Brother Rabbit decides to	Brother Bear

34. What is the moral of the story?

_____

_____

_____

_____

_____

WRITING SKILLS

☼ Semester Checkpoint
Learning Coach Instructions
Reading Comprehension and Analysis

Explain that students are going to show what they have learned this semester.

1. Give students pages LC22–LC37 of the Semester Checkpoint.

2. Read the directions on the students' pages together. Use the Learning Coach instructions on pages LC19–LC21 to administer the Checkpoint.

3. Use the Answer Key to score the Checkpoint, and enter the results online.

4. Review each exercise with students. Work with students to correct any exercise they missed.

"At the Sea-side"

Part 1. Book Walk Assess whether students take you on a Book Walk of the poem that includes some of the following elements:

1. Identify the writing as a poem.

2. Identify elements of poetic structure, such as lines and stanzas.

3. Read the title aloud.

4. Use the title to make a prediction about the poem.

5. Describe the illustration.

6. Use the illustration to make a prediction about the poem.

Part 2. Reading Comprehension Have students read the poem on their own and answer the multiple choice comprehension questions. Tell students they may use the poem to answer the questions.

"Goober Peas"

Part 3. Book Walk Assess whether students take you on a Book Walk of the article that includes some of the following elements:

12. Identify the writing as a story or article, not poetry or drama.

13. Identify the use of paragraphs, instead of lines or stanzas.

14. Read the title aloud.

15. Use the title to make a prediction about the selection.

16. Describe the illustration.

17. Use the illustration to make a prediction about the selection.

Part 4. Reading Comprehension Have students read the article on their own and answer the multiple choice comprehension questions.

"The Stone in the Road"

Part 5. Book Walk Assess whether students take you on a Book Walk of the story that includes some of the following elements:

24. Identify the writing as a story, not poetry or drama.

25. Identify the use of paragraphs, instead of lines or stanzas.

26. Read the title aloud.

27. Use the title to make a prediction about the story.

28. Describe the illustration.

29. Use the illustration to make a prediction about the story.

Part 6. Reading Comprehension Have students read the story to themselves and answer the multiple choice comprehension questions.

Part 7. Literary Analysis Have students complete the questions about the story.

LITERATURE & COMPREHENSION

☼ Semester Checkpoint
Reading Comprehension and Analysis

At the Sea-side

Robert Louis Stevenson

When I was down beside the sea
A wooden spade they gave to me
To dig the sandy shore.
My holes were empty like a cup.
In every hole the sea came up,
Till it could come no more.

spade: shovel

Part 1. Book Walk

Do a book walk of "At the Sea-side" aloud.

1.–6.

Part 2. Reading Comprehension

Read the questions about "At the Sea-side" and choose the answer.

7. What is the rhyme scheme of the poem?

   A. The rhyme scheme is AABBB.

   B. The rhyme scheme is ABCABC.

   C. The rhyme scheme is AABAAB.

   D. The rhyme scheme is AABCCB.

8. How many beats, or syllables, are there in lines 1, 2, and 4?

   A. 4

   B. 6

   C. 8

   D. 10

9. How old is the speaker?

   A. The speaker is a baby.

   B. The speaker is a child.

   C. The speaker is an adult.

   D. The speaker is an old person.

10. Who most likely gave the speaker the spade?

   A. workers at the beach

   B. children at the beach

   C. the speaker's parents or other adults

   D. a teacher from school

11. How does the water get into the holes?

   A. It comes from the sea.

   B. The speaker puts it in.

   C. It comes from a bucket.

   D. The holes fill up when it rains.

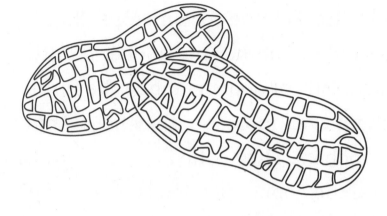

Goober Peas

Have you ever eaten a goober pea? Maybe you have without even knowing it. A goober pea is what we usually call a peanut.

Many years ago, the goober came to America from Africa. It was an easy plant to grow. American farmers liked the goober plant. But, cotton was still their main crop.

Planting cotton year after year caused a problem. It wore out the soil. George Washington Carver told farmers they should plant goobers one year, then cotton the next, then go back to goobers. Rotating their crops in this way would help the farmers have good crops and it would help the soil.

Once, some very pesky insects called boll weevils attacked the cotton crops. But, the insects did not bother the goober plants. This characteristic of goobers made the farmers like them even more. So, they began planting more goobers. They called them peanuts, because the goober pea looks like a small nut.

When goobers are growing, you can see only the plant, not the peanuts. Do you know why? The peanuts grow underground.

First, flowers grow on the short, bushy plant. Then, the flowers send stalks down into the soil. Under the ground, little pods grow on the stalks. Inside the pods, you will find the goober peas, or peanuts. To gather the peanuts, farmers dig up the entire plant. A peanut fresh from the plant tastes like a fresh green pea.

When the goober peas are roasted, then you get the crunchy treat that people enjoy at the circus and baseball games. Who would have guessed that something with such a funny name could taste so good!

LITERATURE & COMPREHENSION

Part 3. Book Walk

Do a Book Walk of "Goober Peas" aloud.

12.–17.

Part 4. Reading Comprehension

Read the questions about "Goober Peas" and choose the answer.

18.　What kind of writing is "Goober Peas"?

　　A. poetry

　　B. drama

　　C. fiction

　　D. nonfiction

19.　What is the topic of "Goober Peas"?

　　A. peas

　　B. plants

　　C. peanuts

　　D. farming

20. What is the main idea of "Goober Peas"?

  A. Americans grow and eat goober peas, or peanuts.

  B. Goober peas came from Africa to America.

  C. George Washington Carver told farmers to plant goobers.

  D. On the goober plant, the peanuts grow underground.

21. Which sentence is a supporting detail of the main idea?

  A. Boll weevils attack cotton crops.

  B. Goober peas are easy to grow.

  C. Goober peas grow inside a pod.

  D. The goober plant is short and bushy.

22. Which sentence is a fact from the article?

  A. Have you ever eaten a goober pea?

  B. The peanuts grow underground.

  C. A peanut fresh from the plant tastes like a fresh green pea.

  D. When the goober peas are roasted, then you get a crunchy treat that people enjoy at the circus and baseball games.

23. Which sentence is an opinion from the article?

A. It was an easy plant to grow.

B. But, the insects did not bother the goober plants.

C. Who would have guessed that something with such a funny name could taste so good!

D. To gather the peanuts, farmers dig up the entire plant.

The Stone in the Road

There once was a king who lived in a beautiful palace in a little village. He loved the people in the village and tried in many ways to help them.

But, the people were often selfish and did not try to help one another. The good king wished to teach them a lesson. So, he arose early one morning and placed a large stone in the road that led past his palace. Then hiding himself nearby, he watched to see what would happen.

Soon, a woman came along with her goats. She complained because the stone was in the way, and stepping over it, she went up the road.

By and by a man came, riding a donkey. He complained about the stone, but rode around it and went on his way.

Other people came and went. Each remarked about the stone, but no one tried to move it.

At last, when the day was almost ended, the miller's boy came down the road. Seeing the stone, he halted and put down the bundle he was carrying.

"This stone should not be here," he said. "Someone might fall over it. I will move it out of the way."

The stone was very heavy, and the boy could scarcely lift it. After many tries, he at last pushed it to one side. As he turned to go on his way, he saw a bag in the place where the rock had been. Something was written on the bag.

Bending closer, he read these words: "This bag of gold belongs to the one who helps others by removing the stone from the road."

The miller's boy carried his treasure homeward with a happy heart. And, as the king returned to his palace, he said, "I am glad that I have found someone who is unselfish enough to think of the comfort of others."

Part 5. Book Walk

Do a Book Walk of "The Stone in the Road" aloud.

24.–29.

Part 6. Reading Comprehension

Read the questions about "The Stone in the Road" and choose the answer.

30. How does the king feel about the people in the village?

    A. He does not ever think about them.

    B. He loves them and tries to help them.

    C. He thinks they are not clever.

    D. He dislikes them and wishes them bad luck.

31. Why does the king put the stone in the road?

    A. He thinks the people are selfish, and he wants to teach them a lesson.

    B. He thinks it will be funny to watch people try to get around the stone.

    C. He thinks it would be a good idea for people to learn a new way into town.

    D. He thinks the people should have a place to sit when they are tired.

32. Which word best describes how the king feels when no one moves the stone?

A. angry

C. tired

B. happy

D. sad

33. Which of the following is a trait of the miller's boy?

A. rude

C. caring

B. lazy

D. wicked

34. What does the miller's boy do that shows this trait?

A. He complains about the stone but doesn't move it.

B. He plays along the way instead of hurrying home.

C. He steals the bag of gold from under the stone.

D. He moves the stone to one side of the road.

LITERATURE &
COMPREHENSION

35. Which is the correct order of events in the story?

   A. The king puts a large stone in the road. The miller's boy moves the stone from the road. The king decides to teach a lesson to the people in the village.

   B. The miller's boy moves the stone from the road. People complain about the stone, but walk by. The king is happy that he had finds someone in the village who is not selfish.

   C. The king decides to teach a lesson to the people in the village. The miller's boy moves the stone from the road. The king is happy that he has found someone in the village who is not selfish.

   D. People complain about the stone, but walk by. The king decides to teach a lesson to the people in the village. The miller's boy moves the stone from the road.

LITERATURE & COMPREHENSION

Part 7. Literary Analysis
Answer the questions about "The Stone in the Road."

36. What happens to the miller's boy because he moves the stone?

_____

37. What is the moral of the story?

_____

_____

38. In the real world, what are some ways that someone might be rewarded for being unselfish?

_____

_____

_____

_____

_____

39. Write about a time when you learned this moral. Tell what happened to you or someone else that shows this lesson.

_____

_____

_____

_____

LITERATURE &
COMPREHENSION

Writing Skills

☼ Unit Checkpoint Learning Coach Instructions Complete Sentences

Explain that students are going to show what they have learned about complete sentences.

1. Give students the Unit Checkpoint pages.

2. Read the directions together. Have students complete the Checkpoint on their own.

3. Use the Answer Key to score the Checkpoint, and then enter the results online.

4. Review each exercise with students. Work with students to correct any exercise that they missed.

WRITING SKILLS

☼ Unit Checkpoint
Complete Sentences

Unit Checkpoint Complete Sentences

WRITING SKILLS

Part 1. Complete Sentences
Choose the complete sentence.

1. **A.** likes toads and frogs

    B. Green toads.

    C. Toads hop across the pond.

2. **A.** A pet hamster.

    B. The cage door opened.

    C. Got loose.

3. **A.** Ling's happy day.

    B. Glides down the slide at the water park.

    C. Everyone comes to the party.

4. **A.** Some spiders spin webs

    B. spiders have eight legs.

    C. Most spiders eat bugs.

5. **A.** Sally walks her dog every day.

   B. Rusty barks at the cats

   C. the cats run up a tree.

6. **A.** We make snack mix.

   B. kim mixes the nuts and fruit.

   C. Adam adds sunflower seeds

Part 2. Sentence Beginnings and Endings
Choose the sentence that begins and ends correctly.

7. **A.** Bill threw the ball

   B. Sally ran to first base.

   C. the catcher dropped the ball.

8. **A.** sam wants to play a game.

   B. He looked in the game box

   C. Lori found a good game to play.

☆ Unit Checkpoint Learning Coach Instructions Kinds of Sentences

Explain that students are going to show what they have learned about kinds of sentences.

1. Give students the Unit Checkpoint pages.

2. Read the directions together. Have students complete the Checkpoint on their own.

3. Use the Answer Key to score the Checkpoint, and then enter the results online.

4. Review each exercise with students. Work with students to correct any exercise that they missed.

✿ Unit Checkpoint
Kinds of Sentences

Part 1. Kinds of Sentences
Which kind of sentence is the sentence?

1. Today is Tuesday.
    A. statement
    B. question
    C. exclamation
    D. command

2. What day comes next?
    A. statement
    B. question
    C. exclamation
    D. command

3. Put your soccer ball in the bag.
    A. statement
    B. question
    C. exclamation
    D. command

4. I can't wait to play soccer!
    A. statement
    B. question
    C. exclamation
    D. command

Name .... Date ....

Part 2. End Marks
Choose the correct end mark for the sentence.

5. I saw a bird in the bush

    A. .

    B. ?

    C. !

6. Was it a blue bird

    A. .

    B. ?

    C. !

7. That is the biggest nest I've ever seen

    A. .

    B. ?

    C. !

8. Are there eggs in it

    A. .

    B. ?

    C. !

9. When will the babies hatch

    A. .

    B. ?

    C. !

10. Put that on the table

    A. .

    B. ?

    C. !

Part 3. Sentence Beginnings and Endings
Which sentence is written correctly?

11. **A.** That is a great idea!

      B. you are my best friend.

      C. where is the picture?

      D. Come quickly

12. **A.** put the box on the table.

      B. What is your answer.

      C. here is my paper.

      D. Did you drop your pencil?

WRITING SKILLS

Unit Checkpoint Learning Coach Instructions Nouns

Explain that students are going to show what they have learned about nouns.

1. Give students the Unit Checkpoint pages.

2. Read the directions together. Have students complete the Checkpoint on their own.

3. Use the Answer Key to score the Checkpoint, and then enter the results online.

4. Review each exercise with students. Work with students to correct any exercise that they missed.

☼ Unit Checkpoint
Nouns

Part 1. Person, Place, or Thing

Write each noun from the word bank in the correct place on the chart.

farmer	bike	ocean
shoe	Lake Oz	nurse

	Person	Place	Thing
1.			

Part 2. Nouns

Which word or words in the sentence is a noun?

2. King Kong is scary and huge.

    A. King Kong

    B. scary

    C. huge

3. Go and stand by the fence.

    A. Go

    B. stand

    C. fence

Name _____ Date _____

Part 3. Capital Letters

Which sentence uses capital letters correctly?

4.   A. Don swims in bear creek.

      B. Don swims in Bear Creek.

      C. don swims in Bear creek.

5.   A. My friend went to Alaska last year.

      B. My friend went to alaska last year.

      C. My friend went to Alaska last Year.

6.   A. Our Tulips bloom in March.

      B. Our Tulips Bloom in March.

      C. Our tulips bloom in March.

WRITING SKILLS

Part 4. Common and Proper Nouns
Choose the answer.

7. Which words are common nouns in this sentence?

   We sat by the river and saw Lake Pearl through the trees.

   A. river, Lake Pearl, trees

   B. river, saw, trees

   C. river, trees

8. Which words are proper nouns in this sentence?

   Jen picked up the paper at the corner of Main Street.

   A. Jen, Main Street

   B. paper, corner, street

   C. Jen, paper, Main Street

Unit Checkpoint Learning Coach Instructions Verbs

Explain that students are going to show what they have learned about verbs.

1. Give students the Unit Checkpoint pages.

2. Read the directions together. Have students complete the Checkpoint on their own.

3. Use the Answer Key to score the Checkpoint, and then enter the results online.

4. Review each exercise with students. Work with students to correct any exercise that they missed.

WRITING SKILLS

Name .... Date ....

☼ Unit Checkpoint
Verbs

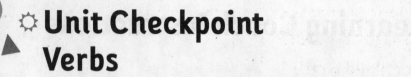

Part 1. Choose the Verb
Choose the verb in the sentence.

WRITING SKILLS

1. The driver parks the car.
    A. driver
    B. parks
    C. car

2. Rain falls on the ground.
    A. Rain
    B. falls
    C. ground

3. My dog is a good friend.
    A. is
    B. good
    C. friend

4. The ball rolls into the street.
    A. ball
    B. rolls
    C. street

5. Birds gather nuts and seeds.
    A. Birds
    B. gather
    C. seeds

Part 2. Action Verbs and Other Verbs
What kind of verb is the underlined word?

6. I <u>say</u> for the dogs to come here.
    A. action verb
    B. not an action verb

7. Bud <u>plays</u> the banjo.
    A. action verb
    B. not an action verb

8. Billy and Betsy <u>are</u> at the fort.
    A. action verb
    B. not an action verb

9. I <u>am</u> happy about the weather.
    A. action verb
    B. not an action verb

WRITING SKILLS

WRITING SKILLS

Part 3. Use Action Verbs

Which underlined word is the correct action verb?

10. **A.** Frank and Fay <u>watching</u> the movie.

     B. Frank and Fay <u>watched</u> the movie.

     C. Frank and Fay <u>watcher</u> the movie.

Unit Checkpoint Learning Coach Instructions
Capitalization and Punctuation in a Letter

Explain that students are going to show what they have learned about capitalization and punctuation in a letter.

1. Give students the Unit Checkpoint pages.

2. Read the directions together. Have students complete the Checkpoint on their own.

3. Use the Answer Key to score the Checkpoint, and then enter the results online.

4. Review each exercise with students. Work with students to correct any exercise that they missed.

WRITING SKILLS

☼ Unit Checkpoint
Capitalization and Punctuation in a Letter

Part 1. Headings of Letters
Which heading is written correctly?

1. **A.** 115 Bay Street
   Clay, New York 13041
   April 6, 2011

   B. 115 Bay Street
   Clay, New York 13041
   April 6 2011

2. **A.** 37 North Elk Street
   Fir Alaska, 67000
   May 27, 2010

   B. 37 North Elk Street
   Fir, Alaska 67000
   May 27, 2010

3. **A.** 1216 Forest road
   Orlando Florida 32819
   March 17, 2011

   B. 1216 Forest Road
   Orlando, Florida 32819
   March 17, 2011

Part 2. Greetings and Closings of Letters
Choose the answer.

4. Which greeting is written correctly?

A. Dear Steve,

B. dear Steve,

C. Dear steve,

D. Dear Steve

5. Which greeting is written correctly?

A. Hello Mr. Lee!

B. Hello Mr. Lee,

C. hello Mr. lee,

D. Hello Mr. Lee

6. Which greeting is written correctly?

A. hi Gretel

B. Hi Gretel

C. Hi Gretel,

D. Hi gretel,

7. Which closing is written correctly?

A. Love

B. love

C. Love,

D. love,

8. Which closing is written correctly?

A. Your Friend,

B. Your friend

C. Your Friend

D. Your friend,

WRITING SKILLS

✲Unit Checkpoint Learning Coach Instructions
Singular and Plural Nouns

Explain that students are going to show what they have learned about singular and plural nouns.

1. Give students the Unit Checkpoint pages.

2. Read the directions together. Have students complete the Checkpoint on their own.

3. Use the Answer Key to score the Checkpoint, and then enter the results online.

4. Review each exercise with students. Work with students to correct any exercise that they missed.

WRITING SKILLS

☼ Unit Checkpoint
Singular and Plural Nouns

Part 1. Identify Singular and Plural Nouns

Choose whether the noun is singular or plural.

1. people
   A. singular
   B. plural

2. axes
   A. singular
   B. plural

3. man
   A. singular
   B. plural

4. geese
   A. singular
   B. plural

5. berries
   A. singular
   B. plural

6. crabs
   A. singular
   B. plural

7. doctors
   A. singular
   B. plural

8. sock
   A. singular
   B. plural

Name _____   Date _____

9. gas
 A. singular
 B. plural

11. grape
 A. singular
 B. plural

10. stars
 A. singular
 B. plural

12. roof
 A. singular
 B. plural

WRITING SKILLS

Part 2. Use Singular and Plural Nouns
Which noun belongs in the sentence?

13. Two ____ waved at me.
 A. boy
 B. boys

16. Mr. Lee cut down four ____.
 A. bushes
 B. bush

14. There are six ____ in the sink.
 A. dishs
 B. dishes

17. I folded the ____.
 A. boxes
 B. boxs

15. All of the ____ like cheese.
 A. mouses
 B. mice

18. Lori hung up both of her ____.
 A. dress
 B. dresses

Part 3. Form Plural Nouns

Choose the correct way to write the plural.

19. What is the correct way to write more than one child?

  A. childs

  B. childrens

  C. children

20. What is the correct way to write more than one foot?

  A. foots

  B. feet

  C. feets

Unit Checkpoint Learning Coach Instructions Subjects and Verbs

Explain that students are going to show what they have learned about subjects and verbs.

1. Give students the Unit Checkpoint pages.

2. Read the directions together. Have students complete the Checkpoint on their own.

3. Use the Answer Key to score the Checkpoint, and then enter the results online.

4. Review each exercise with students. Work with students to correct any exercise that they missed.

☼ Unit Checkpoint
Subjects and Verbs

Unit Checkpoint Learning C
Subjects and Verbs

Part 1. Subjects and Verbs
Circle the subject in the sentence. Underline the verb.

1. The drum beats.

2. Three horns toot.

3. A harp plays.

4. A banjo strums.

5. Something crashes.

Part 2. Agreement
Choose the sentence that is correct.

6. **A.** The paint spill on the ground.

    B. The colors makes a mess.

    C. Jack wipes it up.

7. **A.** The book is on the table.

    B. The library are not open today.

    C. Those books was overdue.

8. **A.** The lawn look green.

    B. The flowers bloom.

    C. Bees buzzes around.

WRITING SKILLS

Unit Checkpoint Learning Coach Instructions Pronouns

Explain that students are going to show what they have learned about pronouns.

1. Give students the Unit Checkpoint pages.

2. Read the directions together. Have students complete the Checkpoint on their own.

3. Use the Answer Key to score the Checkpoint, and then enter the results online.

4. Review each exercise with students. Work with students to correct any exercise that they missed.

WRITING SKILLS

☼ Unit Checkpoint
Pronouns

Part 1. Choose the Pronoun

Choose the best pronoun to replace the underlined word or words.

1. <u>Evan</u> made an ant farm.
   A. He
   B. Him
   C. It

2. The ants ran from <u>Evan</u>.
   A. his
   B. him
   C. I

3. <u>Angela</u> is my sister.
   A. You
   B. She
   C. His

4. <u>The gerbil</u> has babies.
   A. It
   B. You
   C. Me

5. <u>The roses and daisies</u> smell good.
   A. We
   B. It
   C. They

6. The taxi stopped for <u>Paul and me</u>.
   A. us
   B. them
   C. I

7. We play <u>the Jets</u> tonight.

    A. him

    B. them

    C. it

8. <u>The Kings</u> play on Saturday.

    A. They

    B. He

    C. Us

9. <u>Chuck and I</u> ate pretzels.

    A. You

    B. We

    C. His

10. This magnet is <u>Bill's</u>.

    A. mine

    B. hers

    C. his

11. The hammers are <u>Sarah's</u>.

    A. his

    B. mine

    C. hers

12. This is <u>Janie's</u> dirty sock.

    A. my

    B. your

    C. her

WRITING SKILLS

☼ Semester Checkpoint
Learning Coach Instructions
Sentences, Nouns, and Verbs

Explain that students are going to show what they have learned about sentences, nouns, and verbs this semester.

1. Give students the Semester Checkpoint: Sentences, Nouns, and Verbs pages.

2. Read the directions together. Have students complete the Checkpoint on their own.

3. Use the Answer Key to score the Checkpoint, and enter the results online.

4. Review each exercise with students. Work with students to correct any exercise they missed.

© K12 Inc. All rights reserved.

WRITING SKILLS

☼ Semester Checkpoint
Sentences, Nouns, and Verbs

Part 1. Complete Sentences
Which group of words is a complete sentence?

1. **A.** Wears a wool hat on winter days.
   B. Was cold and damp outside the tent.
   C. Snow fell all morning.

2. **A.** Lou heard a noise and ran away.
   B. Saw something scary in the bushes.
   C. The night that was dark.

Part 2. Sentence Beginnings and Endings
Which sentence begins and ends correctly?

3. **A.** Where is my glove!
   B. where is my glove.
   C. Where is my glove?

4. **A.** betty got a new bike.
   B. Betty got a new bike!
   C. betty got a new bike?

Part 3. Kinds of Sentences

Choose the sentence that is the kind of sentence listed.

5. Which sentence is a statement?

    A. Can we go to the circus?

    B. I'd love to see the elephants!

    C. We have a front row seat.

6. Which sentence is an exclamation?

    A. I saw your older brother today.

    B. Is he home for a visit?

    C. His hair is so long now!

7. Which sentence is a question?

    A. Why did the chicken cross the road?

    B. He did it to get to the other side.

    C. That's not a good joke!

8. Which sentence is a command?

    A. I'm sorry my room is messy.

    B. I've been so busy!

    C. Move those clothes and sit down.

Part 4. Nouns

Choose the noun or nouns in the sentence.

9. Kevin dances and sings really well.

   A. Kevin

   B. dances

   C. sings

   D. well

10. Come into the office and sit down.

    A. Come

    B. into

    C. office

    D. sit

11. Barry and Liz took the blue bus into town.

    A. Barry, Liz, bus, town

    B. took, bus, into, town

    C. Liz, took, bus, town

WRITING SKILLS

Part 5. Capital Letters

Which sentence uses capital letters correctly?

12. **A.** I opened the door for sue.

    B. i opened the door for Sue.

    C. I opened the door for Sue.

13. **A.** Mount Etna is actually a volcano.

    B. Mount Etna is actually a Volcano.

    C. Mount etna is actually a volcano.

Part 6. Verbs

Which word is the verb in the sentence?

14. Sasha runs five miles every day.

    A. Sasha

    B. runs

    C. miles

    D. day

15. That mirror is very large.

    A. mirror

    B. is

    C. very

    D. large

WRITING SKILLS

Semester Checkpoint
Learning Coach Instructions
Letters, Nouns, Subjects & Verbs, and Pronouns

Explain that students are going to show what they have learned about capitalization and punctuation in letters, singular and plural nouns, subjects and verbs, and pronouns this semester.

1. Give students the Semester Checkpoint: Letters, Nouns, Subjects & Verbs, and Pronouns pages.

2. Read the directions together. Have students complete the Checkpoint on their own.

3. Use the Answer Key to score the Checkpoint, and enter the results online.

4. Review each exercise with students. Work with students to correct any exercise they missed.

Name .... Date ....

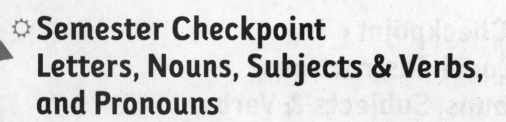

☼ Semester Checkpoint
Letters, Nouns, Subjects & Verbs, and Pronouns

Part 1. Headings
Which heading is written correctly?

1. **A.** 415 Bell Avenue
   Ames, Iowa 50010
   December 20, 2010

   B. 415 Bell avenue
   Ames, Iowa, 50010
   December 20, 2010

2. **A.** 488 Briarhill Road
   Alta, Utah, 84092
   August, 19 2010

   B. 488 Briarhill Road
   Alta, Utah 84092
   August 19, 2010

Part 2. Greetings and Closings
Which greeting or closing is written correctly?

3. **A.** Dear Jenny!
   B. Dear Jenny.
   C. Dear Jenny,

4. **A.** Hello Mr. Richards
   B. Hello mr. Richards,
   C. Hello Mr. Richards,

5. **A.** Thank you,
   B. Thank you–
   C. Thank You.

Part 3. Singular and Plural Nouns

Choose the sentence with the kind of noun listed.

6. Which underlined word is a singular noun?

   A. The dog's <u>feet</u> are wet.

   B. Move the <u>chairs</u> away from the window.

   C. I like the yellow and blue <u>couch</u>.

   D. Jack has a new set of <u>beds</u>.

7. Which underlined word is a plural noun?

   A. That <u>rat</u> is huge!

   B. The <u>bus</u> stops in front of the mall.

   C. Did you see the cute <u>puppies</u>?

   D. I saw a black and white <u>kitten</u>.

8. Which underlined word is a plural noun?

   A. The white <u>goose</u> honked loudly.

   B. Kari is wearing a pretty lace <u>dress</u>.

   C. The <u>circus</u> is coming to town next week.

   D. The <u>mice</u> made soft noises.

9. Which underlined word is correct in the sentence?

   A. Please hand me some <u>hammer</u>.

   B. Please hand me some <u>hammers</u>.

   C. Please hand me some <u>hammered</u>.

WRITING SKILLS

Part 4. Identify Subjects and Verbs

Circle the subject and underline the verb in the sentence.

10. A fish swims.

11. The waves crash.

12. Tony and Maria dance.

Part 5. Match Subject to Verbs

Which verb goes with the subject?

13. Which sentence uses the correct verb?

   A. One horse is brown and white.

   B. One horse are brown and white.

14. Which sentence uses the correct verb?

   A. The cowboys rides over the hill.

   B. The cowboys ride over the hill.

Part 6. Pronouns
Which pronoun can replace the underlined word or words?

15. Bill gave a letter to <u>Jeff</u>.

   A. them

   B. him

   C. her

16. <u>Kelly</u> wanted to read it, too.

   A. She

   B. Her

   C. They

17. Then <u>Sasha and Ellen</u> asked to see it.

   A. we

   B. you

   C. they

18. Can you give it to <u>Will and me</u> next?

   A. us

   B. them

   C. they

19. It's not for <u>George's</u> sister.

   A. their

   B. him

   C. his

20. The letter is <u>Lisa's</u>.

   A. ours

   B. hers

   C. theirs

WRITING SKILLS

Unit Checkpoint Learning Coach Instructions Adjectives

Explain that students are going to show what they have learned about adjectives.

1. Give students the Unit Checkpoint pages.

2. Read the directions together. Have students complete the Checkpoint on their own.

3. Use the Answer Key to score the Checkpoint, and then enter the results online.

4. Review each exercise with students. Work with students to correct any exercise that they missed.

Unit Checkpoint
Adjectives

Part 1. Identify the Adjective
Choose the adjective in the sentence.

1. Which underlined word is an adjective?

   The hot sun beats down on the land.

   A. hot

   B. sun

   C. down

   D. land

2. Which underlined word is an adjective?

   The dish held pieces of soft cheese.

   A. dish

   B. pieces

   C. soft

   D. cheese

3. Which underlined word is an adjective?

   Four bees flew around the flowers in the garden.

   A. Four

   B. flew

   C. flowers

   D. garden

4. Which underlined word is an adjective?

   The plant at the side of the house was a tall cactus.

   A. plant

   B. house

   C. was

   D. tall

5. Which underlined word is an adjective?

   The deer crossed the curvy road.

   A. deer

   B. crossed

   C. curvy

   D. road

Part 2. Use Adjectives
Choose the sentence with the correct adjective.

6. Which sentence uses the correct adjective?

   A. The kitten has a <u>hot</u> purr.

   B. The kitten has a <u>quiet</u> purr.

7. Which sentence uses the correct adjective?

   A. Kim's team wore <u>blue</u> hats.

   B. Kim's team wore <u>cold</u> hats.

8. Which sentence uses the correct adjective?

   A. I see <u>ten</u> stars in the sky.

   B. I see <u>left</u> stars in the sky.

9. Which sentence uses the correct adjective?

   A. A <u>bent</u> apple is often red.

   B. A <u>ripe</u> apple is often red.

Part 3. Use Articles
Choose the sentence with the correct article.

10. Which sentence is correct?

    A. A octopus has eight arms.

    B. An octopus has eight arms.

11. Which sentence is correct?

    A. The crow is a black bird.

    B. The crow is an black bird.

12. Which sentence is correct?

    A. Leroy is a hardest worker on the team.

    B. Leroy is the hardest worker on the team.

WRITING SKILLS

Unit Checkpoint Learning Coach Instructions
Adverbs

Explain that students are going to show what they have learned about adverbs.

1. Give students the Unit Checkpoint pages.

2. Read the directions together. Have students complete the Checkpoint on their own.

3. Use the Answer Key to score the Checkpoint, and then enter the results online.

4. Review each exercise with students. Work with students to correct any exercise that they missed.

WRITING SKILLS

☼ Unit Checkpoint
Adverbs

Part 1. Identify the Adverb

Choose the word in the sentence that is an adverb.

1. Which word in the sentence is an adverb?

   Tyra sleepily sat at the breakfast table.

   A. Tyra   **C.** sat

   B. sleepily   **D.** breakfast

2. Which word in the sentence is an adverb?

   Yellow bees buzzed busily around the hive.

   A. Yellow   **C.** busily

   B. buzzed   **D.** hive

3. Which word in the sentence is an adverb?

   My football team won the big game today.

   A. football   **C.** big

   B. won   **D.** today

Part 2. Adverbs That Tell When

Complete the sentence with an adverb that tells when.

4. Please visit _____.

   A. soon

   B. happily

   C. twice

   D. alone

5. I arrived _____ to practice.

   A. sick

   B. eager

   C. late

   D. tired

Part 3. Adverbs That Tell How

Complete the sentence with an adverb that tells how.

6. Meg _____ looked down.

   A. often

   B. shyly

   C. always

   D. later

7. I ate _____ at dinner.

   A. yesterday

   B. today

   C. early

   D. quickly

WRITING SKILLS

Part 4. Adverb or Adjective?

Look at the underlined word. Decide if it is a verb or a noun.
Then, answer the question.

8. Which sentence uses an adverb or adjective correctly?

    A. We ate the entire <u>pie</u>.

    B. We ate the entirely <u>pie</u>.

9. Which sentence uses an adverb or adjective correctly?

    A. Trees <u>grow</u> slow.

    B. Trees <u>grow</u> slowly.

10. Which sentence uses an adverb or adjective correctly?

    A. Sally is a nice <u>girl</u>.

    B. Sally is a nicely <u>girl</u>.

11. Which sentence uses an adverb or adjective correctly?

    A. I like soft <u>pillows</u>.

    B. I like softly <u>pillows</u>.

12. Which sentence uses an adverb or adjective correctly?

    A. The lions <u>roar</u> loud.

    B. The lions <u>roar</u> loudly.

Unit Checkpoint Learning Coach Instructions Verb Tense

Explain that students are going to show what they have learned about verb tense.

1. Give students the Unit Checkpoint pages.

2. Read the directions together. Have students complete the Checkpoint on their own.

3. Use the Answer Key to score the Checkpoint, and then enter the results online.

4. Review each exercise with students. Work with students to correct any exercise that they missed.

☼ Unit Checkpoint
Verb Tense

Part 1. Future Tense and Past Tense
Choose the answer.

1. Which sentence has a verb that shows an action that will happen later?

    A. Chuck washes his car.

    B. Chuck will wash his car.

    C. Chuck has washed his car.

2. Which sentence has a verb that shows an action that will happen later?

    A. Diana's plane will land today.

    B. Diana's plane lands today.

    C. Diana's plane landed today.

3. Which sentence has a verb that shows an action that already happened?

    A. Many soldiers live on the base.

    B. Many soldiers lived on the base.

    C. Many soldiers will live on the base.

Part 2. Present Tense
Choose the answer.

4. Which sentence has a verb that shows an action that is happening now?

   A. A fire burns on the side of the road.

   B. A fire will burn on the side of the road.

   C. A fire burned on the side of the road.

5. Which sentence has a verb that shows an action that is happening now?

   A. Ian laughed at the joke.

   B. Ian laughs at the joke.

   C. Ian had laughed at the joke.

6. Which sentence has a verb that shows an action that is happening now?

   A. Amy and Mia will walk to the park.

   B. Amy and Mia walked to the park.

   C. Amy and Mia walk to the park.

7. Which sentence has a verb that shows an action that is happening now?

   A. They had won the game.

   B. They win the game.

   C. They will win the game.

WRITING SKILLS

Part 3. Irregular Past Tense Verbs

Choose the answer that shows an action that already happened.

8. Which sentence uses the correct verb to show an action in the past?

    A. I writed you a long letter.

    B. I wrote you a long letter.

    C. I wroted you a long letter.

    D. I written you a long letter.

9. Which sentence uses the correct verb to show an action in the past?

    A. Katie running fast.

    B. Katie runned fast.

    C. Katie ranned fast.

    D. Katie ran fast.

10. Which sentence uses the correct verb to show an action in the past?

    A. Vic telled the best stories.

    B. Vic tolded the best stories.

    C. Vic telling the best stories.

    D. Vic told the best stories.

11. Which sentence uses the correct verb to show an action in the past?

    A. The baby sitted down.

    B. The baby satted down.

    C. The baby sat down.

    D. The baby sitting down.

Unit Checkpoint Learning Coach Instructions Quotations

Explain that students are going to show what they have learned about quotations.

1. Give students the Unit Checkpoint pages.

2. Read the directions together. Have students complete the Checkpoint on their own.

3. Use the Answer Key to score the Checkpoint, and then enter the results online.

4. Review each exercise with students. Work with students to correct any exercise that they missed.

WRITING SKILLS

WRITING SKILLS

☼ Unit Checkpoint Quotations

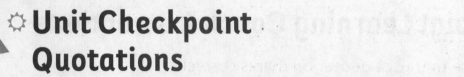

Part 1. Spot the Quotations
Identify the sentence that has a quotation.

1. Which sentence has a quotation?

   A. Eve said that the old house looks brand new.

   B. Eve thought that the old house looked brand new.

   C. Eve was telling me that the old house looks brand new.

   D. Eve said, "This old house looks brand new."

2. Which sentence has a quotation?

   A. Her mother told her to take a picture.

   B. Her mother asked if she'd take a picture.

   C. "Take a picture," her mother said.

   D. Her mother wanted to know if she'd take a picture.

3. Which sentence has a quotation?

   A. "That fireplace used to be so dirty!"

   B. That fireplace used to be so dirty!

   C. I shouted that the fireplace used to be so dirty.

   D. Tom mentioned that the fireplace used to be so dirty.

Part 2. Use Quotation Marks

Identify the sentence that uses quotation marks correctly.

4. Which sentence is correct?

   A. The runner gasped "Where is the finish line?

   B. The runner gasped, "Where is the finish line?"

   C. The runner gasped Where is the finish line?"

   D. "The runner gasped, Where is the finish line?"

5. Which sentence is correct?

   A. Tony moaned Nancy gets to do everything."

   B. Tony, "moaned," Nancy gets to do everything.

   C. Tony moaned, "Nancy gets to do everything."

   D. "Tony moaned," Nancy gets to do everything.

6. Which sentence is correct?

   A. A reporter spoke up, "I write for the local paper.

   B. A reporter spoke up I write for the local paper."

   C. "A reporter spoke up," I write for the local paper.

   D. A reporter spoke up, "I write for the local paper."

7. Which sentence is correct?

    A. I sighed, "I have to get up early tomorrow."

    B. I sighed I have to get up early tomorrow."

    C. "I sighed," "I have to get up early tomorrow."

    D. I sighed, "I have to get up early tomorrow.

Part 3. Insert Quotation Marks

Place quotation marks where they belong in the sentence.

8. Bob said, I'll race you to the lake.

9. Aunt Marie asked, What time does the party begin?

10. Ted answered, It will start at noon.

Unit Checkpoint Learning Coach Instructions Possessive Nouns

Explain that students are going to show what they have learned about possessive nouns.

1. Give students the Unit Checkpoint pages.

2. Read the directions together. Have students complete the Checkpoint on their own.

3. Use the Answer Key to score the Checkpoint, and then enter the results online.

4. Review each exercise with students. Work with students to correct any exercise that they missed.

WRITING SKILLS

☼ Unit Checkpoint
Possessive Nouns

Part 1. Spot the Possessive Nouns
Choose the answer.

---

1. Which word in the sentence is a possessive noun?

   The mayor's speech lasted two hours.

   A. mayor's   **C.** lasted

   B. speech   **D.** hours

2. Which word in the sentence is a possessive noun?

   Soon all of the kids' eyelids grew heavy.

   A. Soon   **C.** eyelids

   B. kids'   **D.** heavy

3. Which word in the sentence is a possessive noun?

   The men's voices weren't very deep.

   A. men's   **C.** weren't

   B. voices   **D.** deep

4. Which word in the sentence is a possessive noun?

   That's why I liked the children's song more.

   A. That's   **C.** liked

   B. I   **D.** children's

LANGUAGE ARTS ORANGE | POSSESSIVE NOUNS

Part 2. Form Possessive Nouns
Choose the answer.

5. Which answer correctly replaces the underlined part of the sentence?

   A <u>shirt Carla has</u> is ripped.

   A. Carlas shirt   **C.** Carlas' shirt

   B. Carla's shirt   **D.** Carlas's shirt

6. Which answer correctly replaces the underlined part of the sentence?

   She took it to <u>the tailor shop her aunt owns</u>.

   A. her aunts' tailor shop   **C.** her aunt's tailor shop

   B. her aunts tailor's shop   **D.** her aunts's tailor shop

7. Which answer correctly replaces the underlined part of the sentence?

   <u>The hive the bees have</u> must be nearby.

   A. The bees' hive   **C.** The bees hive

   B. The bees's hive   **D.** The bee's hive

8. Which answer correctly replaces the underlined part of the sentence?

Is that buzzing from <u>the movement of their wings</u>?

A. their wing's movement

B. their wings movement's

C. their wings's movement

D. their wings' movement

9. Which answer correctly replaces the underlined part of the sentence?

<u>The feet of cattle</u> are called hooves.

A. Cattles feet

B. Cattle's feet

C. Cattles' feet

D. Cattle feet's

10. Which answer correctly replaces the underlined part of the sentence?

They are very different from <u>the feet of people</u>.

A. peoples' feet

B. peoples feet

C. people's feet

D. people feets

Unit Checkpoint Learning Coach Instructions
Names, Initials, and Titles

Explain that students are going to show what they have learned about capitalizing the names of people and places. They will also show what they learned about writing initials and shortening the titles of people.

1. Give students the Unit Checkpoint pages.

2. Read the directions together. Have students complete the Checkpoint on their own.

3. Use the Answer Key to score the Checkpoint, and then enter the results online.

4. Review each exercise with students. Work with students to correct any exercise that they missed.

☼ Unit Checkpoint
Names, Initials, and Titles

Part 1. Find the Correct Sentence
Choose the correct sentence.

1. Which sentence is written correctly?

    A. She did not see aunt Alice until after dinner.

    B. She did not see aunt alice until after dinner.

    C. She did not see Aunt Alice until after dinner.

    D. She did not see Aunt alice until after dinner.

2. Which sentence is written correctly?

    A. Then, Mrs. carlow stopped by to say hello.

    B. Then, Mrs. Carlow stopped by to say hello.

    C. Then, mrs. Carlow stopped by to say hello.

    D. Then, mrs. carlow stopped by to say hello.

3. Which sentence is written correctly?

    A. Sue wrote S.NR. for her initials.

    B. Sue wrote s. n. r. for her initials.

    C. Sue wrote snr. for her initials.

    D. Sue wrote S. N. R. for her initials.

Part 2. Shorten the Titles
Choose the correct sentence.

4. Which sentence correctly shortens the underlined words?

   How is <u>Reverend Vernon</u> doing?

   A. How is rev Vernon doing?

   B. How is Rev. Vernon doing?

   C. How is rev. Vernon doing?

   D. How is Rvrnd. Vernon doing?

5. Which sentence correctly shortens the underlined words?

   I haven't seen him or <u>Mister Williams</u> all summer.

   A. I haven't seen him or Mstr. Williams all summer.

   B. I haven't seen him or mr. Williams all summer.

   C. I haven't seen him or Mr. Williams all summer.

   D. I haven't seen him or Mr Williams all summer.

6. Which sentence correctly shortens the underlined words?

You didn't tell me they went to see <u>Doctor Brown</u>.

 A. You didn't tell me they went to see Dr. Brown.

 B. You didn't tell me they went to see dr. Brown.

 C. You didn't tell me they went to see Dr Brown.

 D. You didn't tell me they went to see Docr. Brown.

7. Which sentence correctly shortens the underlined words?

I thought <u>Miss Yates</u> went to Texas.

 A. I thought ms Yates went to Texas.

 B. I thought Mss. Yates went to Texas.

 C. I thought Ms Yates went to Texas.

 D. I thought Ms. Yates went to Texas.

8. Which sentence correctly shortens the underlined words?

The people cheered for <u>Governor Ruth Alda</u>.

 A. The people cheered for Gov Ruth Alda.

 B. The people cheered for Gvr. Ruth Alda.

 C. The people cheered for Gov. Ruth Alda.

 D. The people cheered for Gvnor. Ruth Alda.

Part 3. Capitalize the Correct Word

Choose the word that should be capitalized.

9. Which underlined word should be capitalized?

You will <u>reach</u> the <u>country</u> of <u>canada</u> if you go <u>north</u> from here.

A. reach

B. country

C. canada

D. north

10. Which underlined word should be capitalized?

You can <u>visit</u> <u>mexico</u> if <u>you</u> head <u>south</u>.

A. visit

B. mexico

C. you

D. south

11. Which underlined word should be capitalized?

Travel toward the <u>ocean</u> and you'll find <u>yourself</u> in a <u>city</u> called <u>boston</u>.

A. ocean

B. yourself

C. city

D. boston

12. Which underlined word should be capitalized?

My <u>cousin</u> lives in a small <u>town</u> in <u>california</u> near a <u>lake</u>.

A. cousin

B. town

C. california

D. lake

Unit Checkpoint Learning Coach Instructions Commas and Apostrophes

Explain that students are going to show what they have learned about using commas to separate words in a list and about forming and using contractions.

1. Give students the Unit Checkpoint pages.

2. Read the directions together. Have students complete the Checkpoint on their own.

3. Use the Answer Key to score the Checkpoint, and then enter the results online.

4. Review each exercise with students. Work with students to correct any exercise that they missed.

WRITING SKILLS

☼ Unit Checkpoint
Commas and Apostrophes

Part 1. Correct Commas
Choose the sentence that uses commas in a list correctly.

1. Which sentence uses commas correctly?

   A. Pizza burgers and sandwiches will be at the party.

   B. Pizza, burgers, and, sandwiches will be at the party.

   C. Pizza, burgers and sandwiches will be at the party.

   D. Pizza, burgers, and sandwiches will be at the party.

2. Which sentence uses commas correctly?

   A. Sherry collects, coins, stamps, and, books.

   B. Sherry collects coins stamps, and books.

   C. Sherry collects coins, stamps, and books.

   D. Sherry collects coins stamps and books.

3. Which sentence uses commas correctly?

   A. The young funny, and, pretty, star won an award.

   B. The young, funny, and pretty star won an award.

   C. The young, funny and pretty, star won an award.

   D. The young, funny and pretty star won an award.

Part 2. Choose the Contraction

Choose the sentence that spells the contraction for the underlined words correctly.

4. You <u>should not</u> try to climb that tree.

   A. You should'nt try to climb that tree.

   B. You shouldn't try to climb that tree.

   C. You shouldnt try to climb that tree.

   D. You shouldnt' try to climb that tree.

5. The hat <u>I am</u> wearing belongs to Dave.

   A. The hat I'm wearing belongs to Dave.

   B. The hat Im wearing belongs to Dave.

   C. The hat I'm' wearing belongs to Dave.

   D. The hat Im' wearing belongs to Dave.

6. <u>You are</u> too young to remember.

   A. Your'e too young to remember.

   B. You'r too young to remember.

   C. Your too young to remember.

   D. You're too young to remember.

Part 3. Write the Contraction

Write the contraction for the underlined words.

7.   Uncle Jake said the snow <u>will not</u> stop tonight.

       _____

8.   I promise that <u>I will</u> be back.

       _____

9.   Sorry, but these <u>are not</u> my dogs.

       _____

10.   Please tell me if <u>she is</u> late.

       _____

11.   It <u>does not</u> matter who wins or loses.

       _____

12.   Do you know if <u>we are</u> next?

       _____

Unit Checkpoint Learning Coach Instructions
More Capital Letters

Explain that students are going to show what they have learned about using capital letters.

1. Give students the Unit Checkpoint pages.

2. Read the directions together. Have students complete the Checkpoint on their own.

3. Use the Answer Key to score the Checkpoint, and then enter the results online.

4. Review each exercise with students. Work with students to correct any exercise that they missed.

Name .... Date ....

☼ Unit Checkpoint
More Capital Letters

WRITING SKILLS

Part 1. Days and Months

Choose the sentence that uses capital letters correctly.

1. Which sentence uses capital letters correctly?

   A. Dad's birthday is in the month of december.

   B. Dad's birthday is in the Month of December.

   C. Dad's birthday is in the month of December.

   D. dad's Birthday is in the month of december.

2. Which sentence uses capital letters correctly?

   A. Can you meet me at noon on Tuesday?

   B. Can You meet me at noon on tuesday?

   C. Can you meet Me at noon on tuesday?

   D. Can you meet me at Noon on Tuesday?

3. Which sentence uses capital letters correctly?

   A. The month of february has the fewest Days.

   B. The month of february has the fewest days.

   C. The Month of February has the fewest days.

   D. The month of February has the fewest days.

Name .... Date ....

Part 2. Holidays and More

Choose the part of the sentence that needs capital letters.

4. Which underlined part of the sentence needs capital letters?

   The <u>football</u> game starts at <u>one</u> <u>o'clock</u> on <u>thanksgiving day</u>.

   A. football

   B. one

   C. o'clock

   D. thanksgiving day

5. Which underlined part of the sentence needs capital letters?

   My <u>cousin</u> played a great <u>april fool's day</u> <u>joke</u> on <u>me</u>.

   A. cousin

   B. april fool's day

   C. joke

   D. me

6. Which underlined part of the sentence needs capital letters?

   Many <u>kids</u> like to drink <u>purpleteeth</u> grape <u>juice</u> with
   their <u>lunch</u>.

   A. kids

   B. purpleteeth

   C. juice

   D. lunch

7. Which underlined part of the sentence needs capital letters?

   The <u>forgi</u> <u>motorcycle</u> that your older <u>brother</u> rides is really <u>cool</u>.

   A. forgi

   B. motorcycle

   C. brother

   D. cool

Part 3. Letter Perfect
Choose the answer.

8. What is the correct way to write the greeting of a letter?

   A. dear uncle vincent,

   B. Dear Uncle vincent,

   C. Dear uncle Vincent,

   D. Dear Uncle Vincent,

9. Which answer corrects the mistake in the sentence?

   Believe it or not, i know that feeling well.

   A. Believe it or not, I know that feeling well.

   B. Believe it or not, i know that Feeling well.

   C. believe it or not, I know that feeling well.

   D. Believe it or not, i know that feeling well.

10. What is the correct way to write the closing of a letter?

   A. see You soon,

   B. See You Soon,

   C. See you Soon,

   D. See you soon,

WRITING SKILLS

Semester Checkpoint
Learning Coach Instructions
Adjectives, Adverbs, Verb Tense, and Quotations

Explain that students are going to show what they have learned about adjectives, adverbs, verb tense, and quotations this semester.

1. Give students the Semester Checkpoint: Adjectives, Adverbs, Verb Tense, and Quotations pages.

2. Read the directions together. Have students complete the Checkpoint on their own.

3. Use the Answer Key to score the Checkpoint, and enter the results online.

4. Review each exercise with students. Work with students to correct any exercise they missed.

☼ Semester Checkpoint
Adjectives, Adverbs, Verb Tense, and Quotations

Part 1. Adjectives
Choose the underlined word that is an adjective.

1. The <u>fox</u> <u>jumped</u> over the <u>brown</u> <u>log</u>.
    - **A.** fox
    - **B.** jumped
    - **C.** brown
    - **D.** log

2. <u>When</u> did the <u>jumbo</u> <u>jet</u> <u>land</u>?
    - **A.** When
    - **B.** jumbo
    - **C.** jet
    - **D.** land

Part 2. Articles
Choose the sentence with the correct article.

3. Which sentence uses articles correctly?
    - **A.** A ant crawled into an hole.
    - **B.** An ant crawled into a hole.
    - **C.** A ant crawled into a hole.

Part 3. Adverbs

Choose the answer.

4. Which sentence has an adverb that tells **how**?

   A. Mrs. Kelly angrily tore up the paper.

   B. Yesterday, Mrs. Kelly tore up the paper.

   C. Mrs. Kelly tore up the yellow paper.

5. Which sentence has an adverb that tells **when**?

   A. We visit my aunt's giant house.

   B. We happily visit my aunt's house.

   C. We often visit my aunt's house.

WRITING SKILLS

Part 4. Adjective or Adverb?
Choose the answer.

6. Which sentence uses the correct word to describe the underlined word?

   A. It was a busy <u>day</u> for me.

   B. It was a busily <u>day</u> for me.

7. Which sentence uses the correct word to describe the underlined word?

   A. Trish <u>ran</u> quick to the corner.

   B. Trish <u>ran</u> quickly to the corner.

Name

Date

Part 5. Verb Tense
Choose the answer.

8. Which sentence tells about a present action?

   A. Kyle will play the trumpet.

   B. Kyle played the trumpet.

   C. Kyle plays the trumpet.

   D. Kyle used to play the trumpet.

9. Which sentence tells about a future action?

   A. She will open the window.

   B. She opens the window.

   C. She had to open the window.

   D. She opened the window.

10. Which sentence tells about a past action?

   A. Jack drops the ball.

   B. Jack dropped the ball.

   C. Jack will drop the ball.

   D. Jack is dropping the ball.

© K12 Inc. All rights reserved.

WRITING SKILLS

11. Which word correctly replaces the underlined word to tell about something that already happened?

I <u>eat</u> fish for dinner on Friday.

 A. ate

 B. eated

12. Which word correctly replaces the underlined word to tell about the past?

The queen <u>keeps</u> crows in her castle.

 A. keeped

 B. kept

Part 6. Quotations
Choose the answer.

13. Which sentence uses quotation marks correctly?

 A. "Bea asked, Is that Darren's dog?"

 B. "Bea asked,""Is that Darren's dog?"

 C. Bea asked, "Is that Darren's dog?"

14. Which sentence uses quotation marks correctly?

 A. Sharon whispered, "Be very quiet."

 B. "Sharon whispered," Be very quiet.

 C. "Sharon whispered, Be very quiet."

Semester Checkpoint
Learning Coach Instructions
Possessive Nouns, Capital Letters, Commas, and Contractions

Explain that students are going to show what they have learned about possessive nouns, capital letters, commas, and contractions this semester.

1. Give students the Semester Checkpoint: Possessive Nouns, Capital Letters, Commas, and Contractions pages.

2. Read the directions together. Have students complete the Checkpoint on their own.

3. Use the Answer Key to score the Checkpoint, and enter the results online.

4. Review each exercise with students. Work with students to correct any exercise they missed.

WRITING SKILLS

WRITING SKILLS

☼ Semester Checkpoint
Possessive Nouns, Capital Letters, Commas, and Contractions

Part 1. Possessive Nouns
Choose the sentence with the correct possessive noun.

1. Which sentence forms the possessive noun correctly?

   A. Where are the cities parks?

   B. Where are the citys' parks?

   C. Where are the citys parks?

   D. Where are the city's parks?

2. Which sentence forms the possessive noun correctly?

   A. Those three birds beaks are hard.

   B. Those three birds' beaks are hard.

   C. Those three bird's beaks are hard.

   D. Those three birds's beaks are hard.

3. Which sentence forms the possessive noun correctly?

   A. My brothers joke that they are part of a men's' club.

   B. My brothers joke that they are part of a mens' club.

   C. My brothers joke that they are part of a men's club.

   D. My brothers joke that they are part of a mens club.

Part 2. Capital Letters
Choose the correct sentence.

4. Which sentence uses capital letters correctly?

   A. I saw Ted on Friday.

   B. I saw ted on friday.

   C. I saw Ted on friday.

   D. I saw ted on Friday.

5. Which sentence uses capital letters correctly?

   A. Is Mother's day always in May?

   B. Is Mother's Day always in May?

   C. Is Mother's Day always in may?

   D. Is mother's day always in May?

6. Which sentence uses capital letters correctly?

   A. we only use Freshclean toothpaste.

   B. we only use freshclean Toothpaste.

   C. We only use Freshclean toothpaste.

   D. We only use freshclean toothpaste.

7. Which sentence uses capital letters correctly?

   A. Your daughter Emma plays on the team that I coach.

   B. your daughter Emma plays on the team that I coach.

   C. Your daughter Emma plays on the team that i coach.

   D. Your daughter Emma plays on the Team that I coach.

8. Which greeting for a letter is written correctly?

   A. Dear mr. Moreland,   C. Dear mr. moreland,

   B. dear Mr. Moreland,   D. Dear Mr. Moreland,

Part 3. Initials and Titles
Choose the answer.

9. What is the correct way to write the initials of the underlined name?

   Michael Patrick Stewart wrote a great book.

   A. M-P-S   C. Mps

   B. MPS.   D. M. P. S.

10. What is the correct way to shorten the underlined title?

    My dentist is Doctor Minnimen.

    A. Dr.   C. Doct.

    B. DR.   D. Dr

Part 4. Commas

Choose the correct sentence.

11. Which sentence uses commas correctly?

    A. The zoo is home to, lions tigers and, bears.

    B. The zoo is home to lions, tigers, and bears.

    C. The zoo is home to lions tigers, and, bears.

    D. The zoo is home to lions, tigers and bears.

Part 5. Contractions

Choose the correct contraction to replace the underlined words.

12. I <u>did not</u> have lunch yet.

    A. I didnt' have lunch yet.

    B. I didno't have lunch yet.

    C. I did'nt have lunch yet.

    D. I didn't have lunch yet.

13. <u>I am</u> sure that Jessica will come.

    A. Im sure that Jessica will come.

    B. I'm' sure that Jessica will come.

    C. I'm sure that Jessica will come.

    D. Im' sure that Jessica will come.